Cover Graphic Design
Thomas Pion
Art: Marco Pennisi & C.

Graphic Designers
Angela Ficarelli
Rafaella Picozzi

Coordinating Editors
Roberta De Pieri
Massimo Marconi

Contributing Editors
Lorena Arpesella
Annamaria Semprevivo

Original text
Claudio Riva
Simona Fati

Cover Design: Marco Ghiglione
Colour elaboration: Flavio Chiumento

Iconographic sources
Centro Documentazione RCS Periodici – Milan
Fototeca Storica Nazionale Ando Gilardi – Milan
Fototeca Gilardi / Leemage
Museo nazionale del Fumetto - Lucca

Literature Classics

Tales from One Thousand and One Nights

SUMMARY

The One Thousand and One Nights,
cover of the Ulrico Hoepli edition in 1939.

**THE MYSTERY AND
MAGIC OF THE PERSIAN
ORIENT ARE BROUGHT
TO LIFE IN THESE
CARTOON PARODIES.**

The One Thousand and One Nights (or *Alf lailha wa lailha* in Arabic), often known as 'Arabian Nights' from the first English language edition in 1706, is the most popular book of Arab literature known in the West. It is a collection of a hundred or so folk tales and other stories written over the centuries by authors who have remained unknown.

Like other oriental works, *The One Thousand and One Nights* is set within a frame story that justifies the numerous tales tangential to it. Betrayed by his wife, King Shahryar of Persia sentences her to death. He then decides that all women are false and that he will spend every night with a different young woman, each of them to be executed the next morning. This cruel ritual is interrupted when it becomes the turn of the shrewd Scheherazade who arouses the King's interest by telling him a fascinating story every night and then, before she reaches the end, inserts the beginning of a new story, leaving the King in suspense.

Curious to find out how each new story ends, Shahryar keeps postponing Scheherazade's execution for another day. This pattern continued for one thousand and one nights until, captivated by her beauty, the king decides to spare Scheherazade's life and take her as his wife. The first of the Disney parodies, *The Adventures of Sinbad the Duck,* is inspired by Sinbad the Sailor. *Ali Donald and the Flying Carpet* parodies elements found in many of the Tales with particular reference to *Aladdin, Ali Baba and the Forty Thieves,* and *The Fisherman and the Genie.*

AND ONE NIGHTS

Sinbad the Sailor recounts the fantastic adventures he has during his seven voyages in the seas east of Africa and south of Asia, visiting magical places, where he faced monsters and encountered supernatural phenomena. Sinbad describes how his life was often at risk during his voyages. On his very first voyage he disembarked on an island which in reality was the back of a whale. When the whale suddenly dived, Sinbad was unable to get back to the ship and found himself alone in the sea. He managed to survive this experience as well.

CAPTAIN DONALD SINBAD, LIKE THE HERO SINBAD, IS A COURAGEOUS AND SUCCESSFUL SAILOR WITH A MERCHANT SHIP CREWED BY HUEY, DEWEY AND LOUIE

7

DONALD SINBAD'S ADVENTURE STARTS WHEN HE FALLS IN LOVE WITH PRINCESS DAISY AMINA, AS SHE PASSES BY IN A SEDAN CHAIR

On another voyage, Sinbad's ship was attacked by a very large number of savages, small in stature and covered in red hair, who took the entire crew prisoner. They were led before a gigantic man with only one eye in the middle of his forehead. This cyclops sized up each of the members of the crew in turn as possible supper. He then fell deeply asleep and Sinbad took advantage of this to get the crew to build a raft. He next took a spit that he held in the fire until the point was red hot, thrust it into the cyclops' eye and blinded him. The sailors then launched the raft, while on shore two giants were throwing large stones aiming to sink it, but to no avail. Sinbad was saved again.

THE EL-BEAG BOYS, THE EASTERN VERSION OF THE BEAGLE BOYS, ARE THE PIRATES IN THE PARODY WHO ATTACK A SHIP CARRYING PRINCESS DAISY AMINA AND HOLD HER FOR RANSOM.

During another voyage, after a lavish banquet, Sinbad fell asleep and was left behind on an island where he encountered a fearsome roc, one of the legendary giant birds reputed to have been able to carry off and eat elephants.

> 66 All of a sudden, the sky became dark, as if a cloud had come over it. Amazed though I was with this darkness, I became even more astounded when I realised that it was caused by a bird of enormous size, bulky body, and wide wings, flying towards me. I remembered a story which travellers and voyagers had told me long before, that there is, in certain of the islands, a bird of enormous size called a roc. I was convinced therefore that the dome which I had seen was one of the eggs of that bird. And lo, the bird alighted upon the dome and brooded over it. 99

THE GIGANTIC CROAK PARODIES THE DANGEROUS ROC THAT APPEARS IN THE STORIES OF SINBAD'S VOYAGES.

Tying his turban to one of the bird's feet, which were as thick as the trunk of a tree, Sinbad was transported to a valley sprinkled with large and marvellous diamonds. Merchants would throw huge chunks of meat into the valley, which the birds carried back to their nests. The men would then drive them off and collect the diamonds stuck to the meat. The wily Sinbad straps one of the pieces of meat to his back and is carried back to the nest along with a large sack full of precious gems. Rescued from the nest by the merchants, he returns home with a fortune in diamonds.

Sinbad and his sailors also encountered a roc's egg on another voyage when they disembarked on a remote island. This enormous egg had almost hatched with the young bird's beak already piercing the shell. Oblivious to Sinbad's warnings, the crew killed, roasted and ate the chick. When the parents found out, they crushed the ship with immense rocks.

> " The birds returned, and we saw that each of them held an immense rock in its claws. When they were exactly above the vessel, they halted, and then one bird loosened its hold and the huge block of stone hurtled through the air, but thanks to the presence of mind of the helmsman, who turned our ship violently in another direction, it fell into the sea close beside us... Unfortunately, the other rock fell with a mighty crash right in the midst of our luckless vessel, smashing it into a thousand fragments. "

All the passengers and crew were killed, though Sinbad managed to survive for the umpteenth time by holding on to a piece of driftwood from the ship until he reached an island. He was eventually rescued by a passing ship and continued homewards.

DONALD SINBAD HAD TO FREE PRINCESS DAISY FROM THE CROAK'S ISLAND AND THREATENED TO MAKE AN OMELETTE OF ITS EGG IN ORDER TO WARD OFF THE PARENT'S ATTACK.

THE ONLY WAY FOR DONALD SINBAD AND DAISY AMINA TO GET OFF THE ISLAND WAS TO JUMP INTO THE SEA.

Sinbad's last voyage took him to the Isle of Serendip, the Sanskrit name for the island country now known as Sri Lanka, as emissary for the Caliph. While returning, his ship was attacked by pirates and he was taken captive and sold as a slave. The merchant who bought him discovered his skill with bow and arrow and sent him out to kill elephants for their valuable ivory tusks. One day the elephants surrounded him and one of them carried him off.

> **"** He carried me to a place where he laid me down on the ground, and retired with all his companions. After having lain some time, and seeing the elephants gone, I got up, and found I was upon a long and broad hill, covered all over with the bones and teeth of elephants. I confess to you that this furnished me with abundance of reflections. I admired the instinct of those animals; I doubted not but that this was their burying place, and that they carried me thither on purpose to tell me that I should forbear to persecute them, since I did it only for their teeth. **"**

Nonetheless, Sinbad was well rewarded by the merchant for showing him this hill and was also given his liberty. He then returned home to a warm welcome from the Caliph.

> **"** I retired very well satisfied with the honours I received and the presents which he gave me; and after that I gave myself up wholly to my family, kindred and friends. **"**

WHEN HE RETURNED WITH PRINCESS DAISY, DONALD SINBAD ALSO RECEIVED A WARM WELCOME FROM THE SULTAN AND GLADSTONE BEY.

AND PRINCESS DAISY AMINA CHOSE CAPTAIN DONALD SINBAD FOR HER HUSBAND.

ALI DONALD AND THE FLYING CARPET

A ROC'S EGG ALSO PLAYS A ROLE IN ANOTHER WELL-KNOWN TALE FROM THE ONE THOUSAND AND ONE NIGHTS.

In the story of Aladdin and his magic lamp, Aladdin is told that the incredible palace that he has commanded the genie of the lamp to build for him and the Princess Badroulbadour is incomplete without the presence of a roc's egg. When he orders the genie to procure one, the reaction is unexpected, but gives him information that he can then use to save his own life by taking that of a hitherto unknown enemy.

❝ The hall shook as if ready to fall; and the genie said, in a loud and terrible voice, 'Is it not enough that I and the other slaves of the lamp have done everything for you, but you, by an unheard-of ingratitude, must command me to bring my master, and hang him up in the midst of this dome? This attempt deserves that you, the princess, and the palace should be immediately reduced to ashes; but you are spared because this request does not come from yourself. Its true author is the brother of the African magician, your enemy whom you have destroyed. He is now in your palace, disguised in the habit of the holy woman Fatima, whom he has murdered. His design is to kill you; therefore take care of yourself.' ❞

WE ARE NOW IN THE MIDDLE OF THE OCEAN!

I CAN SEE SOME FABULOUS BEACHES ON THE HORIZON!

YOU'RE WRONG, UNCLE!

HIS NEPHEWS PERSUADE ALI SCROOGE TO BUY A BOAT AND GO OFF TO LOOK FOR A JAR THAT WILL BE COMFORTABLE FOR MUSTAFA.

IN THE PARODY, THE GENIE IS CALLED MUSTAFA AND HE PREFERS TO LIVE IN A JAR, BUT ALI-DONALD HAS BROKEN IT AND MUSTAFA CAN'T FIND ANOTHER ONE THAT FITS.

Ali Baba is another famous character from One Thousand and One Nights. One day, out in the forest, he hid from forty horsemen, whom he recognized as bandits.

> 66 Their captain went a little way among some bushes, stopped and uttered the words 'Open Sesame!' Suddenly a door opened in the face of the rock. The robbers went inside, stayed some time and then came out, closing the door by saying 'Shut Sesame'. When they were gone, Ali Baba repeated the magic spell, and went into the cave where he saw rich merchandise, and gold and silver in heaps. 99

UNCLE ALI SCROOGE USES THE BUOYANCY POTION HE BOUGHT SO THAT THE ALI-DUCKS AND MUSTAFA CAN WALK ON WATER AND AVOID PAYING CONTOWN'S HUGE EMBARKATION TAX.

THE SIX OF THEM REACH AN ISLAND, BUT ARE CHASED OFF BY MONKEYS THROWING COCONUTS AT THEM.

He took as many bags of gold as his three donkeys could carry and returned home. His brother Cassim got wind of Ali Baba's suddenly found riches and threatened to inform against him if he was not let in on the secret. Ali Baba told him everything, and the day after Cassim used the magic spell to enter the cave. However, carried away by emotion at the great wealth he saw, he forgot the spell for getting out of the cave.

When the thieves returned to the cave, they killed Cassim. Ali Baba recovered his brother's body, but when the thieves discovered it had vanished together with a few bags of gold, they decided the only way to save their secret was to find and kill the person who knew it. They eventually found out that Ali Baba was their man, and devised a plan to kill him. Their captain went to Ali Baba's house disguised as a merchant with jars of oil large enough for his men to hide inside.

Margiana, Ali Baba's slave, got wind of the scheme, and poured boiling oil in each jar, killing all the thieves. The captain of the band fled, but later, bent on revenge, he went back in disguise. Once again, the sly Margiana discovered the plot. She performed several dances to distract the bandit so that she could approach him. She then drew a dagger and plunged it into his heart. A few days later, Margiana, now freed from slavery, married Ali Baba's son. They all lived happily ever after becoming richer and richer thanks to the treasure of the cave.

As in Aladdin and the Forty Thieves, there is also a genie in a story about the adventures of a poor, old fisherman. One day, he found a copper jar in his net.

IN FREETOWN, EVERYTHING IS FREE!

THEY ARE EXTREMELY RARE AND VERY MUCH IN DEMAND!

EH?

SCROOGE DISCOVERS THAT COCONUTS ARE A RARE SPECIALITY AND GETS AN IDEA

13

66 Presently, there issued from it thick smoke, which rose up gradually and when it was all out of the jar, condensed into a solid body and became a monstrous, gigantic genie of such enormous proportions that the fisherman wanted to flee; but he was so upset and so dismayed, that his legs were trembling and he could not get them to move. **99**

HERE IT IS… A FLYING CARPET. WITH THIS, YOU CAN GET ABOUT EVERYWHERE VERY EASILY!

!

BEAUTIFUL!

THE INVENTOR THEY MET EARLIER NOW OFFERS THEM—A FLYING CARPET!

It's the El-Beag Boys!

Come right in! Do you remember us?

Ha! Ha!

When Ali-Donald lands the carpet and its passengers, the El-Beag Boys tell them to hand over the money from the coconuts.

The genie had been imprisoned in the jar for centuries and had sworn to kill whoever freed him. The fisherman saved himself by feigning disbelief that such a huge genie could get back into the jar. The genie fell for the trick and was again enclosed. The fisherman threatened to throw the jar back in the sea, but the genie swore he would bring wealth to the fisherman if he would keep him. He led the man to a pond where he caught four fish: one white, one red, one blue and one yellow.

I'll see if it fits me...

Mustafa suddenly sees just the right jar for him and vanishes inside; his voice from 'nowhere' gives the El-Beag boys the fright of their lives.

66 **Carry them to the Sultan and present them to him, and he will give thee what shall enrich thee. But do not fish here more than once a day, otherwise you will come to evil.** 99

So the fisherman took the fish to the Sultan, who was amazed with those beautiful specimens and bought them from him. When the Sultan found out that the fish were also magic he asked the old man to bring him to the pond. There he also discovered the palace of a king whose body had been turned into black marble from the waist down. The Sultan found a way to break the spell, the king married the Sultan's beautiful daughter and the fisherman, who had been the cause of these happy events, was showered with gifts and riches and lived happily ever after with his family. So the genie was as good as his word in making the fisherman's fortune.

AND SO, DONALD DUCK STARTED READING THE ADVENTURES OF HIS DISTANT ANCESTOR, DONALD SINBAD THE DUCK...

"WE FINALLY REACHED THE PORT OF THE CALIPHATE, HAVING LOST ALL OUR CARGO IN A TERRIBLE STORM..."

THERE'S ABSOLUTELY NOTHING LEFT! WHAT ARE WE GOING TO DO NOW, CAPTAIN DONALD SINBAD?

THE SHIP IS IN URGENT NEED OF REPAIRS!

WE'LL FIND OTHER GOODS TO TRANSPORT AND WE'LL BE ABLE TO SET SAIL AGAIN SOON!

NOT EVEN THE MOST SAVAGE STORM CAN DAUNT DONALD SINBAD!

THAT'S TRUE. BUT HE'S ALWAYS LOSING THE MERCHANDISE THAT HE'S GIVEN RESPONSIBILITY FOR!

THE VOYAGES ARE **FULL** OF ADVENTURES, BUT OUR POCKETS ARE **EMPTY**!

IT IS CERTAINLY NOT THE DESIRE FOR RICHES THAT DRIVES OUR CAPTAIN TO SAIL THE SEVEN SEAS!

In fact, Sultan Scrooge Hassan had already received the demand for ransom from the El-Beag boys...

WHY DIDN'T WE BRING THE SOLDIERS THE SULTAN PLACED AT OUR DISPOSAL?

IT SEEMS THAT BEING FEW IN NUMBER, AND WITH THE ELEMENT OF SURPRISE, WE'LL STAND A BETTER CHANCE OF SUCCEEDING! THAT'S WHAT HE SAYS, ANYWAY...

STEADY AS SHE GOES TOWARDS THOSE ISLANDS. THE PIRATES CAN'T BE FAR OFF!

THE EL-BEAG BOYS GANG IS INFESTING THESE WATERS, AND I HAVE TO ROOT THEM ALL OUT! DO YOU KNOW ANYTHING ABOUT THEM?

NOBLE CAPTAIN... WE ARE ONLY **POOR** FISHERMEN!

SAY NO MORE! HERE'S SOMETHING TO HELP **CONVINCE** YOU!

THE PIRATES ARE HIDING OUT ON THE THIRD ISLAND ON THE RIGHT!

LET'S GO! ONWARD!

WE MUST BE ON OUR GUARD! THIS COULD BE DANGEROUS!

SHORTLY AFTER...

IT'S FINALLY GIVING WAY!

WELL DONE! THIS WAY, THE CURRENT WILL CARRY IT OUT TO SEA!

MEANWHILE, ON LAND...

HEY, YOU! WHAT ARE YOU DOING HERE?

I'D LIKE TO ASK FOR SOME INFORMATION... I'VE LOST MY WAY AND...

WHAM!

WE'LL FIND THE PRINCESS THERE, FOR SURE!

WHAT ABOUT THE OTHER PIRATES? LET'S HOPE THEY'RE SLEEPING!

"FORTUNATELY, THEY WERE! DONALD SINBAD AND HIS CREW TIED THEM UP AS THEY SLEPT..."

THERE! THAT'S THE LAST OF THEM SECURED!

WHERE COULD THE PRISONERS BE?

ZZZZ

ALL SHIPS STAY AWAY BECAUSE THE MONSTER SINKS ANY VESSEL THAT DRAWS TOO CLOSE!

I **HAVE** TO FIND IT! IT'S MY DUTY TO FIND IT!

THAT'S MADNESS! BUT IF YOU HAVE NO REGARD FOR YOUR LIFE, JUST FOLLOW THAT COURSE!

AND SO, A FEW DAYS LATER...

THERE'S THE ISLAND!

JUST AS THEY SAID, BUT THERE'S NO WAY TO DISEMBARK!

ONE WHIRLPOOL AFTER ANOTHER AND BARE ROCK AT THE BASE! IT'S IMPOSSIBLE TO REACH THE TOP!

UNLESS, YOU HAVE A NICE PAIR OF WINGS!

AND THERE'S SOMETHING ELSE! COME HAVE A LOOK!

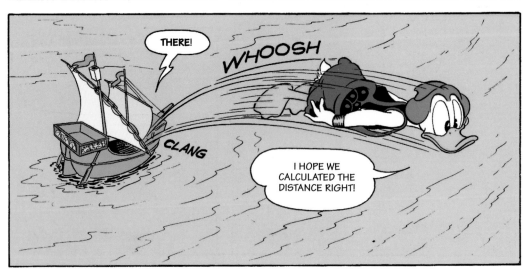

PERFECT! I'VE **ALMOST** REACHED...

... MY DESTINATION. OUCH! OUW!!

HELLO, SAILOR! WHO ARE YOU? HAVE YOU COME TO FREE ME?

I AM DONALD SINBAD, MY PRINCESS!

THE WINGED MONSTER IS NOT HERE, I TAKE IT?

IT WENT AWAY AT DAWN, BUT IT WILL SOON RETURN...

AND WHAT IS THAT?

THE CROAK'S EGG! IT'S HATCHING! WE MUST GET AWAY FROM HERE, NOW!

AT THAT MOMENT...

FLAAP   FLAAAPP

THE CROAK'S COME BACK! WE'RE DONE FOR! WHAT ARE WE GOING TO DO NOW?

A WELL AIMED MISSILE HITS THE CROAK!

42

DONALD SINBAD MADE MANY OTHER VOYAGES, BUT ALWAYS RETURNED TO HIS BELOVED WIFE.

WHAT AN EVENTFUL AND ADVENTUROUS LIFE THAT DONALD SINBAD HAD!

THAT'S A FINE WAY TO DUST!

FORGIVE ME, UNCLE! BUT I FOUND THIS OLD MANUSCRIPT AND I SIMPLY COULDN'T PUT IT DOWN!

YOU ALWAYS FIND EXCUSES FOR DOING NOTHING! LET ME SEE!

HERE YOU ARE! IT'S REALLY MOVING!

HMM! I'D FORGOTTEN I HAD THIS BOOK... BUT IT'S REALLY INTERESTING!

54

56

68